ZAP ZERO THE DESPATCH RIDER

Diane Wilmer

Illustrated by Paul Dowling

COLLINS

Zap Zero's had a heck of a day!

He has been taking messages . . .

. . . picking up parcels . . .

. . . delivering mail.

"Blimey! It's about time I had a holiday," says Zap.

It's the intercom.

"Zap Zero to Control. Zap Zero to Control. I'm at Marble Arch. Free and cruising. Where next?"

"No problem," answers Zap.
"Where's the pick-up?"

"OK!" says Zap. "See you when I get back."

It's a big, lumpy parcel with bits sticking out all over the place.

"Coo! I've never seen one like this before," says Zap.

He whizzes across the city, waving to all the other despatch riders as he goes.

"Hey! I'm off to Scotland!"

"Lucky guy," they call back.
"Take it easy, Zap."

Zipping out of London.

Zooming down the motorways.

Zapping over bridges.
Curling round the junctions.

Bouncing over green hills.
Green, rolling, northern hills.

"YIPPEE!" sings Zap.
"Baa Baa," go the sheep.

"EEK YAHZAH BLOOOH!" goes the parcel.

“Funny business?” thinks Zap and stops the bike. He pokes the parcel.

“Nothing there, must be blooming hearing things,” he says and carries on.

In the high mountains Zap starts to sing at the top of his voice.

"Zap Zero. Zap Zero.
The man on the bike.
Zap Zero. Zap Zero.
I go where I like.
I flash around England
and whirl across Wales
and now I'm in Scotland
to blaze a new trail."

"EEK YAHZAH BLOOH!" goes the parcel.

Night falls.
The road gets steeper and steeper
and the noise gets louder and creepier.
"EEK YAHZOOH BLOOH!"
The sound echoes across the valleys
and rolls up to the mountain tops,
where it shivers against the stars.

It even makes the sheep jump.
"Baaa-ah! Baaa-ah!" they bleat.

"Twit-a-woo!" hoot the owls
from the tree tops.

"EEK YAHZOOH BLOOH!" goes the parcel.
"Oh, I've had enough of all this spooky stuff,"
says Zap.

He stops at the next transport caff and has
beans, chips, sausage and eggs.
“Just what I need,” says Zap.
“A nice, hot supper and a bit of a chat.”
It’s warm and steamy in the caff.
Everybody’s chatting and joking,
the jukebox is roaring and the
one-armed bandits are flashing.

A song comes on the jukebox
and Zap starts to tap his feet
and sing along with the music.

One man claps his hands and
another starts to whistle.

A girl with pink hair and big boots jumps up and dances round with her boyfriend.

"Eeh, I could stay here all night," sighs Zap, "but there's work to do."

"Cheers, lads!" he calls.
"See you," everybody calls back.

It's cold and dark outside.
The rain soaks him to the skin and the wind nearly blows him back to London.
"Shiver my sprockets, I'm freezing!" groans Zap.

"EEK YAHZAH BLOOOH!" goes the parcel.
"Shut up, you squealing windbag!"
bellows Zap.

But the noise goes on and on.
It will not go away.
On the flat roads and going uphill there
is no noise at all but when Zap zips
downhill – what a racket!

"EEK YAHZAH BLOOH!"
"What's in that blooming parcel?" shouts Zap, but he doesn't stop again. He keeps on going until the sun comes up.

By the time he reaches Edinburgh he is tired and cross.
"And I've got earache," moans Zap.

But at last the parcel is quiet.
Zap drives through the empty streets to the grey castle on the hill.

“Parcel for Fergus McFiddock,” he says.

“You’ll find wee Fergus up on the battlements,” says the guard on the gate.

Nine pipers stand on the battlements
puffing and blowing at the strangest
looking things Zap has ever seen.
"Parcel from London!" he yells.
"Och, that'll be for you, Fergus,"
calls the sergeant.

Fergus McFiddock opens the parcel and jigs around until his kilt twirls.

"My bagpipes!" he cries.
"My beautiful, beautiful bagpipes!"

As Zap drives away a lovely sound
bursts out of the castle and fills
the morning sky.

"Now that's what I call music,"
says Zap and heads back to the big city.